THE CANNIBAL FAMILY OF SAWNEY BEAN AND STORIES OF SOUTH-WEST SCOTLAND

Illustrated by John Mackay

"The Cannibal Family of Sawney Bean and Stories of South West Scotland"
was first published in 1991 by Lang Syne Publishers, Ltd,
45 Finnieston Street, Glasgow. Tel: 0141 204 3104.
Reprinted 1993
Reprinted 1995
Reprinted 1996

Printed by Dave Barr Print
45 Finnieston Street, Glasgow
Tel: 0141 221 2598

ISBN 185217 1596

INTRODUCTION

In these pages we tell the chilling story of Sawney Bean and his hellish clan of cannibals. Between them they murdered and ate over one thousand travellers, snatched from the remote highways and byways of Galloway in the 16th century. Many innocent innkeepers, falsely accused of robbing their guests and disposing of the bodies, met their end on the hangman's rope. But eventually a fatal error trapped the Beans and the grim secrets of their seaside cave were exposed to a shocked world.

And we also uncover other dark tales from the south-west's stirring past.

• Find out about the murder hole on the moor that sucked 50 victims to quick deaths in the unfathomable deep.
• Find out about the ice curse that wiped out a family.
• Read a Covenanter officer's shocking eye witness account of the bloody battle of Drumclog.
• See what life was like for smugglers and the daring escapades they mounted to dodge the law. Much blood was spilled as contraband was moved on land and sea.
• See how a castle garrison was brought to its knees.
• Read the remarkable opinions of a traveller to the region in 1723. He found "gravity in every face .... owing to their praying and frequent long graces which give their looks a religious cast." He complained his room at the inn had not been washed for 100 years and was shocked at a total absence of any cooked food on the Sabbath. Sunday dinner consisted of bread, butter, and an egg. He reports that the most common names locally were Maxwell and MacLellan.

All the stories, and the poem, The Hills of Galloway, have been selected and adapted from a 19th century book on the traditional stories of south-west Scotland.

The wicked family who ate 1,000 travellers

Artist John Mackay's impression of Sawney Bean

Hundreds of travellers who vanished without trace in sixteenth century Galloway sparked off one of Galloway's most baffling mysteries. Where could they have gone? And why did the disappearances continue after the suspected culprits, usually innocent innkeepers, had been hanged?

There were many theories and tales of supernatural influence. But when the true reason was eventually discovered it caused a sensation, not just in Galloway but throughout Scotland.

For hundreds of men, women and children had been robbed, murdered and EATEN by a family called Bean. The incredible story began when Sawney Bean was born in an East Lothian village, some nine miles east of Edinburgh, in the reign of James I of Scotland. His father was a hedger and ditcher and brought up his son to the same laborious employment.

He got his daily bread in his youth by these means, but being idle and not caring to be confined to any honest employment, he left his father and mother, and ran away to a remote part of the country, taking with him a woman who was similar to himself.

They set up home in a cave on the shore of Galloway, where they lived for 25 years, without going into any city, town or village.

During this time they had a great number of children and grandchildren, whom they brought up after their own manner, without any notions of humanity or civil society. They never kept any company, but among themselves, and supported themselves entirely by robbing. Furthermore, they never robbed anyone, whom they did not murder.

As soon as they had robbed any man, woman or child, they used to carry off the carcase to the den, where cutting it into quarters, they would pickle the mangled limbs, and afterwards eat it. This was their only sustenance. They commonly had a surplus of this abominable food, and during the night they frequently threw legs and arms of the unhappy wretches they had murdered into the sea. The limbs were often washed up by the tide in several parts of the country, to the astonishment and terror of all.

Local people were alarmed at such an uncommon loss of their neighbours and acquaintances. Spies were frequently sent into the area, many of whom never returned again, and those who did, after the strictest search, could not find anything out of the ordinary.

Several honest travellers were arrested on suspicion and wrongfully hanged on flimsy evidence: several innocent innkeepers were executed, for no other reason than that the missing persons had stayed with them. Rough justice was executed with the greatest severity imaginable. So many innkeepers, who lived on the western road of Scotland, left the business, for fear of being hanged by mistake.

This, on the other hand, inconvenienced travellers, who could not now find accommodation when they wanted to refresh themselves and their horses, or take up lodging for the night. In a word, the whole country was almost depopulated.

Still the king's subjects were as much missed as before, so that it puzzled the whole kingdom how suvch villanies could be carried on, and the perpetrators not discovered. A great many had been executed, but not one of them made a confession at the gallows. All maintained to the last, that they were perfectly innocent of the crime for which they suffered.

When the magistrates found all was in vain, they left off these rigorous proceedings, and trusted wholly to Providence for a solution.

Sawney's family was by now very large, and every branch of it as soon as able, assisted in perpetrating their wicked deeds, which they still followed with impunity. Sometimes they would attack four, five or six, footmen together, but never more than two, if they were on horseback. They were so careful, that no one whom they had set upon should escape, that an ambush was set on every side to secure them. How was it possible they should be detected, when the only people who saw them never lived long enough to tell the tale?

The place which they lived in was quite solitary and lonesome, and, when the tide came up, the water went two hundred yards into their subterraneous habitation, which reached almost a mile underground. People sent to search all the places round about never supposed any human being would reside in such a place of perpetual horror and darkness.

The number of people these savages destroyed was never exactly known; but it was generally computed that in the twenty-five years they continued their butcheries, they had washed their hands in the blood of at least a thousand men, women and children.

They were at last discovered thus: Late one evening in the year 1600, a man and woman were attacked by members of the Bean clan as they made their way home from a country fair. The man fought bravely against them with sword and pistol, riding some of them down with his horse.

In the conflict the poor woman fell, and was instantly butchered before her husband's eyes. The female cannibals cut her throat, and fell to sucking her blood with as great a gust, as if it had been wine. This done, they ripped up her belly, and pulled out all her entrails. Such a dreadful spectacle seemed to give the husband almost superhuman strength to resist.

Then twenty or thirty who had been at the same fair, came together in a body; on seeing them Sawney Bean and his blood thirsty clan withdrew and made the best of their way through a thick wood to their den.

The man told the whole company what had happened, and showed them the horrid spectacle of his wife, whom the murderers had dragged some distance. They were all struck with stupefaction and amazement, and they took him to Glasgow where he told the full horrific story to the magistrates of that city. They immediately sent to the king.

Three days later his majesty, with four hundred men, set out for Galloway. The man who had been attacked was the guide, and care was taken to have a large number of blood-hounds with them, for defence.

No sign of any habitation was to be found for a long time and even when they came to the wretches' cave, they took no notice of it; but some of the blood-hounds luckily entered the den, and instantly set up a most hideous barking, howling and yelping. The king, with his attendants, came back, and looked in. They could not tell how anything human could be concealed in a place where they saw nothing but darkness; nevertheless, as the blood-hounds increased their noise they went farther in, and refused to come back again; they then began to imagine something or other must live there. Torches

Burned to death!

were immediately sent for, and a great many men ventured in, through the most intricate turnings and windings, till at last they arrived at the human flesh-eaters' living quarters.

They were all so shocked at what they saw that they were almost ready to sink into the earth. Legs, arms, thighs, hands and feet of men, women and children were hung up in rows, like dried beef; a great many limbs laid in pickle, and a great mass of money both gold and silver, with watches, rings, swords, pistols, and a large quantity of clothes, both linen and woollen, and an infinite number of other things which they had taken from those they had murdered, were thrown together in heaps or hung up against the sides of the den.

Sawney's family, at this time, besides himself, consisted of his wife, eight sons, six daughters, eighteen grand-sons, and fourteen grand-daughters, who were all born through incest.

All were seized and secured. The searchers then took what human flesh they could find, and buried it in the sands. They then loaded up the spoils, and returned to Edinburgh with their prisoners. People appeared all along the route to see the cursed tribe. When they came to their journey's end, the Beans were committed to the Tolbooth. Next day they were taken, under a strong guard, to Leith, where they were executed without trial, so clear cut was the damnable evidence against them.

The men were dismembered, their hands and legs were cut from their bodies, leaving them to bleed to death in a few hours. The wife, daughters, and grand-children were made to watch and were later burnt to death in three fires. They all died without the least signs of repentance, cursing to the very last gasp of life.

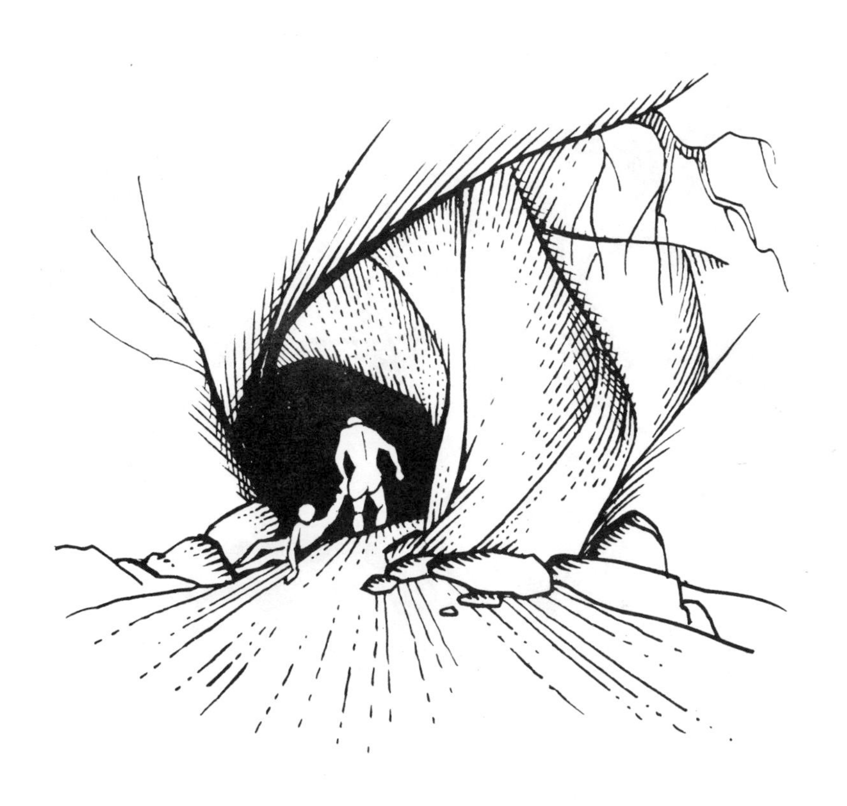

Bean clan attack

Inside the Cave of Horror

Sawney Bean throws another victim on the pile

News of Bean arrests

Murder hole on moor swallowed 50 victims

Some 500 years ago, in a remote district between Ayrshire and Galloway, a moor of apparently boundless extent stetched several miles along the road. It wearied the eye of the traveller by the sameness and desolation of its appearance. Not a tree varied the prospect, not a shrub enlivened the eye by its freshness, nor a native flower bloomed to adorn this ungenial soil. There was nothing to mark that any mortal had ever visited the scene before, except a few huts that were scattered near its centre; and a pathway for those whom business or necessity obliged to pass in that direction.

At length, deserted as this wild region had always been, it became still more gloomy. Strange rumours arose that travellers had been murdered here. When several persons, who were known to have passed that way, mysteriously disappeared, the enquiries of their relatives led to a full investigation: but though the officers of justice were sent to scour the country, and question the inhabitants, not a trace could be obtained of the persons in question nor of any place of concealment which could be a refuge for the lawless or desperate. As the disappearance of individuals became more frequent, the simple inhabitants of the neighbouring hamlet were agitated by the most terrible fear. Some declared that the death-like stillness of the night was often interrupted by sudden cries of more than mortal anguish. One evening a shepherd, who had lost his way on the moor, declared he had approached three mysterious figures, who seemed to be struggling against each other with supernatural energy. Finally, one of them, with a frightful scream, suddenly sank into the earth.

Gradually the inhabitants deserted their homes on the heath, and settled in distant quarters. In time only one of the cottages remained occupied, by an old woman and her two sons. Travellers who used this road now generally did so in groups, to protect each other: and if night overtook them, they generally stopped at the humble cottage, where cleanliness compensated for want of luxury, and where over a blazing fire of peat, the bolder spirits smiled at the imaginary terrors of the road, and the timid trembled as they listened to the tales of terror with which their hosts entertained them.

One gloomy and tempestuous night in November, a pedlar boy anxiously crossed the moor. He prayed that his journey would end safely and was in a state of great terror. Then he saw a light in the distance and presumed it must be the cottage of the old woman where he had lodged the year before. The pedlar boy remembered that a large party of travellers, staying there at the time, had entertained each other with 'frightening' stories. He recollected, too, how anxious the old woman and her sons had been to detain him when the other travellers were departing; and now, therefore, he confidently anticipated a cordial and cheerful reception.

His first call for admission went unanswered, then suddenly the greatest noise and confusion broke out inside the cottage. They think it is one of the supernatural visitants of whom the old Lady talks so much, thought the boy, approaching a window, where the light within showed him all the occupants at their several occupations. The old woman was hastily scrubbing the stone floor, and covering it thickly with sand, while the two sons seemed with equal haste to to be thrusting something large and heavy into an immense chest, which they carefully locked.

The boy thoughtlessly tapped at the window, when they all instantly looked up with angry faces. He shrank back in shock, but before he had time to reflect a moment longer, one of the men suddenly darted out of the door and seized him. "I am not what you take me for" said the boy, attempting to laugh, "but

The boy taps on the window seeking lodgings

only the poor pedlar who visited you last year." "Are you alone?" enquired the old woman in a harsh deep tone. 'Yes," said the boy, "I am alone here; and alas!" he added with a burst of uncontrollable feeling, "I am alone in the wide world also! Not a person exists who would assist me in distress, or shed a single tear if I died this very night." "Then you are welcome!" said one of the men with a sneer.

It was with a shiver of apprehension, rather than of cold, that the boy drew towards the fire, and the looks which the old woman and her sons exchanged, made him wish that he had preferred the shelter of any one of the roofless cottages which were scattered nearby rather than trust himself among such odd people. He was absolutely petrified but tried to conceal his fears from them.

The room to which he retired for the night had a confused and desolate aspect; the curtains seemed to have been violently torn down from the bed, and still hung in tatters around it — the table seemed to have been broken by some violent means, and the fragments of various pieces of furniture lay scattered on the floor. The boy begged that a light might burn till he was asleep. He anxiously examined the fastenings of the door but they seemed to have been wrenched asunder on some former occasion, and were still left in that condition.

Drifting in and out of sleep he fancied himself again wandering on the heath, which appeared to be peopled with spectres, who all beckoned him not to enter the cottage. As he approached it, they vanished with a hollow and despairing cry. The scene then changed, and he found himself again seated by the fire, where the men scowled at him, and the old woman suddenly seized him by the arms, and pinioned them to his side. Suddenly the boy was startled from these agitated slumbers by what sounded like a cry of distress; he was wide awake in a moment, and sat up in the bed — but the noise was

The terrified boy sees blood seeping under the door

not repeated, and he tried to convince himself it was only part of the dream. But he then glanced towards the door and saw blood spilling through the gap at the bottom towards him.

He crept from the bed and spied on the family through the door. Imagine his relief on seeing it was only a goat which they had slaughtered.

But it was only short-lived when he then heard a conversation which transfixed him to the spot.

"This is an easier job than you had yesterday," said the man who held the goat. "I wish all the throats we've cut were as easily and quietly done. Did you ever hear such a noise as the old gentleman made last night! It was well we had no neighbours within a dozen miles, or they must have heard his cries for help and mercy."

"Don't speak of it," replied the other; "I was never fond of bloodshed."

"Ha! Ha!" said the other with a sneer, "you say so, do you?"

"I do," answered the first gloomily; "the Murder Hole* is the thing for me — that tells no tales — a single scuffle — a single plunge — and the fellow is dead and buried to your hand in a moment. I would defy all the officers in Christendom to discover any mischief there."

"Ay, Nature did us a good turn when she contrived such a place as that. Who that saw a hole in the heath, filled with clear water, and so small that the long grass meets over the top of it, would suppose that the depth is unfathomable, and that it conceals more than forty people who have met their deaths there? It sucks them in like a leech!"

"How do you mean to despatch the lad in the next room?" asked the old woman in an undertone. The elder son made her a sign to be silent, and pointed towards the door where their trembling guest was concealed; while the other, with an expression of brutal ferocity, passed the bloody knife across his throat.

The pedlar boy possessed a bold and daring spirit, but in any open resistance the odds were so completely against him that a quick getaway seemed his best recourse. He crossed to the window, and broke the rusty bolt by which the casement had been fastened. He let himself down without noise or difficulty. He was trying to decide which direction to take when the men suddenly called out, "The boy has fled — let loose the blood-hound!" These words sank like a death knell in his heart, and, in a state of absolute terror, he fled across the heath. Soon the baying of the blood-hound broke the stillness of the night, and the voice of his masters sounded through the moor, as they endeavoured to accelerate its speed. Panting and breathless the boy ran on, but every moment his pursuers seemed to gain upon his failing steps.

At full speed, the terrified boy fell over a heap of stones, and having nothing on but his shirt, he was severely cut in every limb. With one wild cry to heaven for assistance, he continued prostrate on the earth, bleeding, and nearly insensible. The hoarse voices of the men, and the still louder baying of the dog, were now so near that instant destruction seemed inevitable. Already he felt himself in their fangs, and the bloody knife of the assassin appeared to gleam before his eyes. But despair renewed his energy, and once more, in an agony that seemed verging towards madness, he rushed forward so rapidly that terror seemed to have given wings to his feet.

Meanwhile the hound had stopped at the place where the pedlar's wounds bled so profusely, and deeming the chase now over it lay down there, and would not move. The men beat it, and tried again to put the hound on the scent — the sight of blood had satisfied the animal that its work was done, and with dogged resolution it resisted every inducement to pursue the same scent a second time.

The pedlar boy in the meantime kept running until dawn.

Ten miles on he reached a village, and spread instant alarm through the neighbourhood — the inhabitants were aroused to a fury. Several of them had lost sons, brothers or friends on the heath, and all united in going immediately to seize the old woman and her sons, whose names were Mackillon. They were nearly torn to pieces by the angry villagers.

Three gibbets were raised on the moor, and the culprits confessed before their execution to the destruction of nearly fifty victims in the Murder Hole which they pointed out, and near which they paid the penalty for their crimes.

The bones of several murdered persons were with difficulty brought up from the abyss — among whom was the father of the pedlar boy.

* An account of this Murder Hole was communicated to Mr George Chalmers, author of *Caledonia*, and is thus referred to in that work, vol iii page 231. — "This Murder Hole is said to be eighty feet deep, from which human bones have been brought forth." The origin of these Murder Holes "have been referred to the feudal grant which conferred the right of Pit and Gallows on so many Barons, the former for the *drowning of women*, the latter for the *hanging of men*."

I was a Covenanter at the Battle of Drumclog

Scotland was in uproar when King Charles I introduced English style church services in 1637. Many Scots regarded Episcopal services as too Catholic in style, and a year later noblemen and gentlemen signed the National Covenant "to prevent Roman Catholicism being brought back to Scotland." But as the years passed matters grew worse with ministers, who refused to accept the new orders, being banned from their parishes. Many of them had to preach under cover at "conventicles", usually held in the hills. Folk who supported them were known as Covenanters, and although opposition spread throughout the country it was particularly strong in Galloway and Ayrshire.

On a May Sunday morning in 1679, at Louden Hill, near the borders of Ayrshire and Lanarkshire, a conventicle was under way when disturbing news arrived. John Graham of Claverhouse, one of the King's most trusted lieutenants and a great hunter of Covenanters, was on his way to break up the service and arrest the worshippers.

But the Covenanters, with 40 horsemen and 200 footmen, decided to fight, and shifted their position to Drumclog, a boggy moor two miles away, where they could fight at a greater advantage.

The battle ended in spectacular victory for the Covenanters. The following account, written by one of their officers, the Laird of Torfoot, was first published in an American newspaper.

It was a fair Sabbath morning, in the summer of 1679, that an assembly of the Covenanters sat down on the heathy mountains of Drumclog. We had assembled not to fight, but to worship the God of our fathers. We were far from the tumult of cities. The long dark heath waved around us; and we disturbed no living creatures, saving the pees-weep and the heather-cock. As usual, we had come armed. For desperate and ferocious hands made bloody raids through the country, and, pretending to put down treason, they waged war against religion and morals. They spread ruin and havoc over the face of bleeding Scotland.

The venerable Douglas had started the solemnities of the day. Our souls were on fire as we remembered our country's sufferings and the wrongs of the church. In this moment of intense feeling, our watchman posted on a neighbouring height fired his carabine and ran towards the congregation. He announced the approach of the enemy. We raised our eyes to the minister. "I have done," said Douglas with his usual firmness. "You have got the theory, now for the practice. You know your duty, self-defence is always lawful. But the enemy approaches." He raised his eyes to heaven and uttered a prayer, brief and emphatic, "Lord, spare the green, and take the ripe."

The officers collected their men, and placed themselves each at the head of his own district. Sir Robert Hamilton placed the foot in the centre, in three ranks. A company of horse, well armed and mounted, was placed on the left; and a small squadron also on the right. These were drawn back, and they occupied the more solid ground, with a view to having a more solid footing, and to arrest any flanking party that might take them on the wings. A deep morass lay between us and the ground of the enemy. Our aged men, our females and children retired; but they retired slowly. They were more concerned for the fate of relatives and of the church, than for their own personal safety. As Claverhouse descended the opposite mountain, they retired to the rising ground in the rear of our host. The aged men walked with their bonnets in hand, their long grey hairs waving to the breeze. They sang a cheering psalm. The music was that of the well-known tune of 'The Martyrs'; and the sentiment breathed defiance. The music floated down on the wind. Our men gave them three cheers as they fell into their ranks. Never did I witness such animation in the looks of men. For me, my spouse and my little children were in the rear. My native plains, and the halls of my father, far below, in the dale of Aven, were in full view from the heights which we occupied. "And these," I said, as Clavers and his troops winded slowly down the dark mountain's side, "these are the unworthy slaves, and bloody executioners, by which the tyrant completes our miseries."

Hamilton was the hero of the hour. His portly figure was seen moving among the ranks. He inspired courage into our raw and undisciplined troops. The brave Hackstone, and Hall of Haughhead, stood at the head of the foot, and re-echoed the sentiments of their Chief. Burley and Cleland had inflamed the minds of the horsemen on the left to great enthusiasm. My small troop on the right needed no exhortations; we were a band of brothers, resolved to conquer or fall.

The trumpet of Clavers sounded a loud note of defiance, and the kettle drum mixed its tumultuous roll. Then they halted and made a long pause. We could see an officer with four file, conducting fifteen persons from the ranks, to a knoll on their left. I could perceive one in black: it was my friend King, the chaplain of Lord Cardross, who had been taken by Clavers at Hamilton. "Let them be shot through the head," said Clavers in his usual dry way, "if they should offer to run away." We could see him view our position with great care. His officers came around him. We soon learned that he wished to do a deal with us. He never offered terms unless he feared that he had met his match; and even then, it was only a manoeuvre to gain time or to deceive. His flag approached the edge of the bog. Sir Robert held a flag sacred; had it been borne by Clavers himself he would have honoured it. He asked the flag-bearer to state his business. "I come,,' said he, "in the name of his sacred Majesty, and of Colonel Graham, to offer you a pardon, on condition that you lay down your arms, and deliver up your ringleaders."

"Tell your officer," said Sir Robert, "that we are fully aware of the deception he practises. He is not clothed with any powers to treat, nor was he sent out to treat with us, and attempt reconciliation. The Government against whom we have risen, refuses to redress our grievances, or to restore us our liberties. Had the tyrant wished to render us justice, he had not sent by the hand of such a ferocious assassin as Claverhouse. Let him, however, shew his powers, and we refuse not to treat: and we shall lay down our arms to treat, provided that he also lay down his. Thou hast my answer." "It is a perfectly hopeless case," said Burley, while he called after the flag-bearer, "Let me add one word by your leave General. Get thee up to that bloody dragoon, Clavers, and tell him, that we will spare his life, on condition that he, Clavers, lays down his arms, and the arms of these troops. We will even let him go on his parole, on condition that he swear never to lift arms against the religion or liberties of his country." A loud burst of applause re-echoed from the ranks; and after a long pause in deep silence, the army sung the following verses of Psalm LXXVI:—

3 'The arrows of the bow he brake,
the shield, the sword, the war,
4 More glorious thou than hills of prey,
more excellent art far.

5 Those that were stout of heart are spoil'd,
they slept their sleep outright;
And none of those their hands did find,
that were the men of might.'

When news of their stand was given to Claverhouse, he cried out with a savage ferocity, "Their blood be on their own

Covenanter spears against mounted cavalry

heads. Be *no quarter* the word this day." His fierce dragoons raised a yell, and "No quarter" re-echoed from rank to rank, while they galloped down the mountain side. It is stated that Burley was heard to say, "Then let it be so, even let there be 'no quarter' — at least in my wing of the host. So God send me a meeting," cried he aloud, "with that chief under the white plume. My country would bless my memory, could my sword give his villainous carcase to the crows."

Our raw troops stood firm at the approach of the enemy; and at the moment when our opponents halted to fire, the whole of our foot dropped on the heath. Not a man was seen down when the order was given to rise, and return the fire. The first flank fired, then kneeling down while the second fired, they made each bullet tell. As often as the lazy rolling smoke was carried over the enemy's heads, a shower of bullets fell on his ranks. Many a gallant man tumbled on the heath. The fire was incessant. It resembled one blazing sheet of flame, for several minutes, along the line of the Covenanters. Clavers attempted to cross the morass, and break our centre. "Spearmen! to the front" I could hear the deep-toned voice of Hamilton say. "Kneel and place your spears to receive the enemy's cavalry; and you, my gallant fellows, fire — *God and our country* is our word." Our officers flew from rank to rank. Not a man gave way that day. As the smoke rolled off, we could see Clavers urging on his men with the violence of despair. His troops fell in heaps around him, and still the gaps were filled up. A frightened trooper would occasionally flinch; but before he could turn or flee, the sword of Clavers was waving over his head. I could see him in his fury, strike both man and horse.

He ordered the flanking parties to take us on the right and left. "In the name of God," he cried, "cross the bog, and charge them on the flanks till we get over the morass. If this fail we are lost."

It now fell to my unit to come into action. Until now we had fired only some distant shots. A gallant officer led his band down to the borders of the swamp, in search of a proper place to cross. We threw ourselves before him and a severe firing began. My gallant men fired with great steadiness. We could see many tumbling from their saddles. Not content with repelling the enemy, we found an opportunity to cross, and attack them sword in hand. The Captain, whose name I afterwards ascertained to be Arrol, threw himself into my path. In the first shock I discharged my pistols. His sudden start in the saddle told me that one of them had taken effect. With one of the tremendous oaths of Charles II, he closed with me. He fired his steel pistol. I was in front of him; my sword glanced on his weapon, and gave a direction to the bullet, which saved my life. By this time my men had driven the enemy before them, and had left the ground clear for single combat. As he made a lounge at my breast, I turned his aside, by one of those sweeping blows, which are rather the dictate of a kind of instinct of self-defence, than a movement of art. As our strokes redoubled, my antagonist's dark features put on a look of deep and settled ferocity. No man who has not encountered the steel of his enemy, in the field of battle, can conceive the looks and manner of the warrior, in the moments of his intense feelings. May I never witness them again! We fought in silence. My stroke fell on his left shoulder; it cut the belt of his carabine, which fell to the ground. His blow cut me to the rib, glanced along the bone, and rid me also of the weight of my carabine. He had now advanced too near to be struck by the sword. I grasped him by the collar. I pushed him backwards; and with an entangled blow of my Ferrara, I struck across his throat. It cut only the strap of his headpiece, and it fell off. With a sudden spring he seized me by the sword belt. Our horses reared and we both came to the ground. We rolled on the heath in deadly conflict. It was in this situation of matters, that my brave fellows had returned from the rout of the flanking party to look after their commander. One of them was actually rushing on my antagonist, when I called on him to retire. We jumped to our feet. Each grasped his sword. We closed in conflict again. After some sharp clashes of steel, I told him my object was to take him prisoner; that sooner than kill him, I should order my men to seize him. "Sooner let my soul be brandered on my ribs in hell,,' said he, "than be captured by a Whigamore. '*No quarter*' is the word of my Colonel, and my word."

"Leave the mad man to me, leave the field instantly," I told my party, whom I could hardly restrain. My sword fell on his left shoulder. His sword dropped from his hand. I lowered my sword, and offered him his life. "*No quarter,*" said he, with a shriek of despair. He snatched his sword, which I held in my hand, and made a lounge at my breast. I parried his blows till he was nearly exhausted; but gathering up his huge limbs, he put forth all his energy in a thrust at my heart. My Andro Ferrara received it, so as to weaken its deadly force; but it made a deep cut. Though I was faint with loss of blood, I left him no time for another blow. My sword glanced on his shoulder, cut through his buff coat, and skin, and flesh; swept through his jaw and laid open his throat from ear to ear. The fire of his ferocious eye was quenched in a moment. He reeled, and falling with a terrible clash, he poured out his soul with a torrent of blood on the heath. I sank down, insensible for a moment. My faithful men who never lost sight of me, raised me up. In the fierce combat, the soldier suffers most from thirst. I stooped down to fill my helmet with the water which oozed through the morass. It was deeply tinged with human blood, which flowed in the conflict above. I started back with horror; and Gawn Witherspoon bringing up my steed, we set forward in the tumult of the battle.

Dragoons are driven into the swamp

All this while, the storm of war had raged on our left. Cleland and the fierce Burley had charged the strong company sent to flank them. These officers permitted me to cross the swamp, then charged them with a terrible shout. "*No quarter,*" cried the dragoons. "Be *no quarter* to you then, ye murderous loons," cried Burley; and at one blow he cut their leader through the steel cap and scattered his brains on his followers. His every blow overthrew a footman. Their whole forces were now brought up, and they drove the dragoons of Clavers into the swamp. They rolled over each other. All stuck fast. The Covenanters dismounted, and fought on foot. They left not one man to bear the tidings to their Colonel.

The firing of the platoons had long ago ceased, and the dreadful work of death was carried on by the sword. At this moment, a trumpet was heard in the rear of our army, there was an awful pause, all looked up. It was only the gallant Captain Nesbit, and his guide, Woodburn of Mains. With a loud Huzza, and flourish of his sword, he placed himself by the side of Burley, and cried, "Jump the ditch, and charge the enemy." He and Burley struggled through the marsh. The men followed as best they could. They formed and marched on the enemy's right flank.

At this instant, Hamilton and Hackstone brought forward the whole line of infantry in front. "*God and our Country,*" re-echoed from all the ranks. "*No quarter*" said the fierce squadrons of Clavers.

I seized the opportunity this moment offered me of making a movement to the left of the enemy to save my friend King and the other prisoners. We came in time to save them. Our swords speedily severed the ropes which tyranny had bound on the arms of the men. The weapons of the fallen foe supplied what was lacking of arms; and with great vigour we moved forward to charge the enemy on the left flank. Claverhouse formed a hollow square — himself in the centre; his men fought gallantly;

they did all that soldiers could do in their situation. Wherever a gap was made, Clavers thrust the men forward, and speedily filled it up. Three times he rolled headlong on the heath as he hastened from rank to rank, and as often he remounted. My little band thinned the ranks. He paid us a visit. Here I distinctly saw the features and shape of this far-famed man. He was small of stature, and not well formed. His arms were long in proportion to his legs; he had a complexion unusually dark; his features were not lighted up with sprightliness, as some had reported; they seemed gloomy as hell: his cheeks were lank and deeply furrowed; his eyebrows were drawn down, and gathered into a kind of knot at their junctions, and thrown up at their extremities; they had, in short, the strong expression given by our painters to those on the face of Judas Iscariot, his eyes were hollow, they had not the lustre of genius nor the fire of vivacity; they were lit up by that dark fire of wrath which is kindled and fanned by an internal anxiety, and consciousness of criminal deeds; his irregular and large teeth were presented through a smile, which was very unnatural on his set of features; his mouth seemed to be unusually large from the extremities being drawn backward and downward — as if in the intense application to something cruel and disgusting; in short, his upper teeth projected from over his under lip, and on the whole, presented to my view the mouth of the Image of the Emperor Julian the Apostate.

In one of his rapid courses past us, my sword could only shear off his white plume and a fragment of his buff coat. In a moment he was at the other side of the square. Our officers eagerly sought a meeting with him. "He has the proof of lead," cried some of our men. "Take the cold steel or a piece of silver." "No," cried Burley, "it is his rapid movement on that fine charger that bids defiance to anything like an aim in the tumult of the bloody fray. I could sooner shoot ten heather cocks on the wing, than one flying Clavers." At that moment Burley, whose eye watched his antagonist, pushed into the hollow square. His blow was levelled at him before he came within his reach. His heavy sword descended on the head of Clavers' horse and felled him to the ground. Burley's men rushed on the fallen Clavers, but his faithful dragoons threw themselves upon them, and by their overpowering force drove Burley back. Clavers was in an instant on a fresh steed. His bugle-man recalled the party who were driving back the flanking party of Burley. He collected his whole troops to make his last and desperate attack — he charged our infantry with such force, that they began to reel. It was only for a moment. The gallant Hamilton snatched the white flag of the Covenant, and placed himself in the forefront of the battle. Our men shouted, "*God and our country*" and rallied under the flag. They fought like heroes. Clavers fought no less bravely. His blows were aimed at our officers. His steel fell on the helmet of Hackstone, whose sword was entangled in the body of a fierce dragoon, who had just wounded him. He was borne by his men into the rear. I directed my men on Clavers; "Victory or death," was the reply to me. Clavers received us. He struck a desperate blow at me as he raised himself, with all his force, in the saddle. My steel cap resisted it. The second stroke I received on my Ferrara and his steel was shiver'd to pieces. We rushed headlong on each other. His pistol misfired — it had been soaked in blood. Mine took effect, but the wound was not deadly. Our horses reared, we rolled on the ground. In vain we sought to grasp each other. In the *mele*, men and horse tumbled on us. We were for a few moments buried under our men, whose eagerness to save the respective officers brought them in multitudes down upon us. By the aid of my faithful man Gawn, I had extricated myself from my fallen horse; and we were rushing on the bloody Clavers, when we were again literally buried under a mass of men; for Hamilton had by this time brought up his whole line, and he had planted his standard where we and Clavers were rolling on the heath. Our men gave three cheers and drove in the troops of Clavers. Here I was borne along with the moving mass of men; and, almost suffocated and faint with the loss of blood, I knew nothing more till I opened my eye on my faithful attendant. He had dragged me from the very grasp of the enemy, and had borne me into the rear, and was bathing my temples with water. We speedily regained our friends; and what a spectacle presented itself! It seemed that I beheld an immense moving mass heaped up together in the greatest confusion. Some shrieked, some groaned, some shouted, horses neighed and pranced, swords rung on the steel helmets. I placed around me a few of my hardy men, and we rushed into the thickest of the enemy in search of Clavers, but in vain. At that instant, his trumpet sounded the loud notes of retreat; and we saw on a knoll Clavers borne away by his men. He threw himself on a horse, and without sword, without helmet, he fled in the first ranks of their retreating host. His troops galloped up the hill in the utmost confusion. My little line closed with that of Burley's, and took a number of prisoners. Our main body pursued the enemy two miles, and splattered the ground with men and horses. I could see the bare-headed Clavers in front of his men, kicking and struggling up the steep sides of Calder hill. He halted only a monment on the top to look behind him then plunged his rowels into his horse, and darted forward; nor did he recover from his panic till he found himself in the city of Glasgow.

"And, my children," the Laird would say, after he had told the adventures of this bloody day, "I visited the field of battle next day; I shall never forget the sight. Men and horses lay in their gory beds. I turned away from the horrible spectacle. I passed by the spot where God had saved my life in the single combat, and where the unhappy Captain Arrol fell, I observed that, in the subsequent fray, the body had been trampled on by a horse and his bowels poured out. Thus my children, the defence of our lives, and the regaining of our liberty and religion, has subjected us to severe trials. And how great must be the love of liberty when it carries men forward, under the impulse of self-defence, to witness the most disgusting spectacles, and to encounter the most cruel hardships of war!"

The Cardoness Castle family wiped out by ice

Three successive lairds went bankrupt trying to build Cardoness Castle, the ruin of which can still be seen today not far from Gatehouse-of-Fleet. And, according to tradition, a fourth laird nearly suffered a similar fate, being obliged at one point to cover the castle with heather.

However in due course matters began to take a turn for the better, and everything seemed to prosper in his hands. The imposing appearance of the Castle had many advantages. It gave standing to the Laird amongst the neighbouring gentry, and inspired confidence in his dependants. The thriving farmer courted his protection with Christmas bullocks and Easter lambs. The cock laird looked up to him as his liege lord, drank his ale, and swore his oaths. The man of mettle with small means, but many wants, who preferred the casual fruits of plunder to the returns of regular industry, found encouragement and employment. The laird rapidly rose in the estimation of his neighbours, added acre to acre and field to field, and at length found himself in possession of a large estate, and at the head of a numerous band of retainers, men of willing heart and ready hand.

Of course the laird had many associates, with whom he could wile away the hours of indolence and inactivity in which most of the time of the gentry of that period was passed. The chief of these companions was Graeme the Border Outlaw, who held a small and nearly ruinous castle at the head of the Vale of Fleet. What the offence was for which he had been obliged to flee was never exactly known. But it was generally believed that he had committed sacrilege by robbing the church of Abbey-Holme of its massive communion plate — a crime in those days considered so heinous, that even the lawless borderers were too afraid to shelter him. He was indeed a man of a profane, scornful spirit, all laws, human and divine, were to him a sport and a mockery.

Such was the man whom the laird delighted to honour. The outlaw, as we have said, was a constant visitor at the castle. The laird had even promised him Marjory, his eldest daughter, in marriage. No wonder then that whispers were sometimes heard that "the laird was nae better than he sud be"; and that fears were often expressed that no good would ever come out of his connection with so desperate and irreligious a character as Graeme.

At this time he had been some twenty years married to a lady, who had brought him a fair fortune, and had blessed his bed with nine children, but to the laird's great mortification they were all daughters. At first he bore the disappointment with some degree of patience, in hopes that fortune would bless him with a son to continue the family name. But as his hopes were successively frustrated by the birth of daughter after daughter, his temper became soured, and he could not help showing resentment against his poor lady. Then when she again fell pregnant he decided that threats might do the trick. He therefore declared that if she should crown his hopes by presenting him with an heir to his name and honours, every kindness should be lavished on herself and her daughters during his life, and that at his death handsome provision should be left for all of them. But if, on the other hand, she produced another daughter he swore by the silver image of the Blessed Virgin at Dundrennan, that he would drown them all in the Black Loch.

Time wore on, and the anxiety of the lady increased. She knew her husband was not a man to use idle threats; and she dreaded the burst of frenzied exasperation that was inevitable if she failed to produce a son.

The laird had promised his eldest daughter in marriage

At length the day of confinement arrived — a day full of expectation to the laird, of anxiety nearly intolerable to the lady. The wise woman of the district, who had witnessed the entrance and exit of more than one generation, had been in attendance for some days so as to be ready at the first call. Everyone was profoundly solicitous about the sex of the unborn babe. For despair predominated over hope. A fearful silence descended over the household. The laird himself paced up and down the great hall with hurried step and restless air. No one dared speak to him. Even his favourite hound, as it caught his eye, slunk out of sight.

Meanwhile things were nearing completion, for the blackest night will usher in the morn — the fiercest tempest be succeeded by a calm. Luckie Richardson had been some hours in the lady's chamber, when the laird heard a shout issue from the room, and immediately afterwards received the joyful announcement that a man-child was born to his house. If the laird was delighted that his greatest wish was now fulfilled, his wife was just greatly relieved. She was freed of a burden that had well nigh crushed her; and she fully participated in the family pride of the laird.

Great were the rejoicings at the castle. Its doors were thrown hospitably open to all comers; gentle and simple alike found a hearty welcome. In the servants' hall the inferior visitors drank, in heady old ale, health and prosperity to the new-born heir; whilst the laird entertained his own friends with racy Bordeaux. And, as parties were very different then, and lasted for weeks, the laird thought there could not be a more appropriate occasion for celebrating the marriage of his daughter with Graeme the outlaw. The laird's opinion was readily accepted; and accordingly, the nuptials took place with all the pomp and solemnity the parties could command. This was another reason for further feasting and mirth. The country was scoured for geese, capons, and turkeys; loch and forest were laid under contribution; and wise men began to shake their heads, and express their fears of a famine. Every in-door amusement and out-door sport was pursued with renewed ardour.

After many more days of fun and games, Graeme and the laird proposed to wind up by giving a sort of carnival fete on the ensuing Sunday. The scene fixed on for the day's amusement was the Black Loch, which was then completely frozen over. All the folk from the surrounding countryside were invited; but, as the day chosen was the Sabbath, and as such festivities were generally considered a desecration of that holy day, few or none attended. And happy would it have been for the laird and his party, had they also remembered to keep the Sabbath-day holy. But the party went on. Every one of the household and family was out on the loch. The infant heir himself was not forgotten. After some hours' sport they sat down to a meal of cold meats with ale and wine. In the midst of drinking a sudden crash was heard: the ice was giving way all around them; chairs, tables and human beings were plunged into the icy water, and not one reached dry land.

Thus perished by one blow the whole family of Cardoness, at a time when all men thought it established for unborn ages. The name perished with them that bore it: and today all that remains of them is this tradition, to warn men of the danger of vanity and not fearing their maker.

The bloody battle for Caerlaverock Castle

A.D.1300

Caerlaverock Castle, on which the old Castle of Ellangowan in *Guy Mannering* is based, stands on the shore of the Solway Firth, about nine miles from Dumfries. It was the seat of the powerful family of Maxwell as early as the reign of Malcolm Canmore, in the eleventh century, when "Evan Macuswell of Caerlaverock" is recorded to have been at the siege of Alnwick in 1093. His successors retained the barony for many generations, distinguishing themselves in the wars of their times, and increasing their influence and hereditary possessions by matrimonial alliances and military services. The origin of this castle, now a massive ruin, and standing in solitude, is uncertain. The Romans possessed a station near it, but history does not record its masters from the sixth to the eleventh century. Its situation and natural defences are such as to have induced the rude inhabitants of the country to select it as a place of strength in those desolating wars and forays, when men had to dispute the possession of their homes with foreign invaders and predatory neighbours.

In the time of Herbert, eleventh Lord Maxwell, the Castle of Caerlaverock was besieged by Edward I, in one of his expeditions to conquer the Scottish nation. He was already in possession of Edinburgh, Stirling, Dunbar, Dundee, Brechin, and Dunnottar; and indeed almost every stronghold between Berwick and the Moray Firth had fallen into his hands. In Dumfriesshire, which, from its frontier situation, severely suffered in these wars, almost every fortress had yielded to him, and probably Caerlaverock was the only remaining retreat of Scottish independence in the country. Edward was determined to take it and the garrison was equally determined to offer a strong resistance.

All the nobility and barons of England, who owed military service, or held of the crown by military tenure, were summoned to Carlisle at the festival of St John the Baptist, A.D.1300, which is celebrated on the 24th of June. A summons had been previously sent to the Castle, demanding its surrender, and the haughty refusal spurred the King to appear before it in person. The royal mandate was punctually obeyed, and never perhaps had the ancient city of Carlisle such an array of royalty and chivalry within its walls. Edward I, one of the greatest princes who ever sat on the throne of England, his son the Prince of Wales, and many other peers and knights, all assembled at the command of their sovereign, whose exasperation against the Scots had been increased by the heroism of Wallace, and their indomitable courage in opposing the English sway.

Edward well knew the strength of Caerlaverock, and the preparations he made for the siege corresponded to the magnitude of the enterprise. As cannon were then unknown, engines of various constructions for discharging large stones, beams of wood, battering rams, robinets, and springalds, were collected from different quarters. Some were brought from Carlisle and Skinburness, others from the Castles of Lochmaben, Jedburgh, and Roxburgh, accompanied by and under the charge of a retinue of engineers, smiths, carpenters, miners, armourers, and other artisans to work the machinery. At that time the English used much the same mode of attack as the Greeks and Romans. The *robinets, springalds,* or espringalls, were the *catapultae* or *balistae* of the ancients — large cross-bows, wrought by machinery, capable of throwing stones, beams, and huge darts; and they were numbered among the heavy military engines of the age. They had also ponderous machines, moving on wheels, resembling the Roman *testudo,* formed with wooden planks, and covered with hides. The machine called a *sow* was of this description, and is thus noticed in an old ballad published in the "Border Minstrelsey":—

> "They laid their sowies to the wall
> Wi' many a heavy peal;
> But he threw o'er to them again
> Both pitch and tar barrell."

In the ancient poem entitled "The Siege of Caerlaverock", and supposed to have been written by Walter of Exeter, a celebrated Franciscan friar, there is an interesting account of the enterprise. About the 1st of July 1300, the English army left Carlisle commanded by Edward I in person, attended by the Prince of Wales, afterwards Edward II, and the most distinguished peers and knights of the kingdom, to the number of eighty-seven. The men at arms amounted to 3000 chosen warriors, and this splendid array of chivalry, which "quite filled the roads to Caerlaverock", presented an imposing spectacle to the rustic peasantry. The poet informs us that they "set forward against the Scots, not in coats and surtouts, but on powerful and noble chargers; and that they might not be taken by surprise, well and securely armed. There were many rich caparisons embroidered on silks and satins, many a beautiful pennon fixed to a lance, and many a banner displayed. And afar off was the noise heard of the neighing of horses; mountains and valleys were covered with sumpter horses, and waggons with provisions, and sacks of tents and pavilions; and the days were long and fine."

The English army was divided into four squadrons, and in this formation they marched by easy journeys into Scotland. The first squadron was commanded by Henry, the "good Earl of Lincoln", namely, Henry de Lacy, a distinguished nobleman, whose name occupies a prominent place in the records of almost every event of his time. John, the "good" Earl of Warren and Surrey, a powerful nobleman and celebrated soldier, headed the second squadron; the third was commanded by Edward in person; and the Prince of Wales, then in his seventeenth year, and bearing arms for the first time, led the fourth. In all these divisions or squadrons were the peers and knights of England, carrying their banners, with pennons streaming, and the whole resembled rather a military triumph than a formidable array to reduce the strong Castle of Caerlaverock.

The exact time of the siege is not mentioned, but it is believed that it must have taken place between the 6th and 14th of July; for it appears from entries in the book of the King's Wardrobe, that Edward was at Dumfries on the 10th of that month, at Caerlaverock on the 13th and 14th, and at Lochrutton on the 17th. During his march, the King visited various churches and shrines, and made many oblations at the altars to ask the saints for success in the enterprise.

At length this imposing array of England's chivalry appeared before Caerlaverock, and the picture of the Castle and its situation was described by Walter of Exeter as follows: — "It was so strong a castle that it did not fear a siege — it was always prepared for its defence whenever it was required with men, engines, and provisions. Its shape was that of a shield (triangular), for it had only three sides all round, with a tower on each angle; but one of them was a double one, so high, so long, and so large, that under it was the gate with the drawbridge, well made and strong, and a sufficiency of other defences. It had good walls and good ditches filled to the edge with water; and I believe there never was a castle more beautifully situated, for at once could be seen the Irish sea towards the west, and to the north a fine country, surrounded by an arm of the sea; so that no creature born could approach it on two sides, without putting himself in danger of the sea. Towards the south it was not easy, because there were numerous dangerous defiles of wood, and marshes, and ditches, where the sea is on each side

The siege of Caerlaverock

of it, and where the river reaches it; and therefore it was necessary for the host to approach it towards the east, where the hill slopes."

As soon as the English army appeared before Caerlaverock, it was formed into three divisions by the King's command. The soldiers began to build huts for their accommodation, of which the poet gives us a very picturesque account — "There might have been seen houses built without carpenters or masons, of many different fashions; and many a cord stretched with white and coloured cloth, with many pins driven into the ground; many a large tree cut down to make huts; and leaves, herbs, and flowers, gathered in the woods, which were strewn within; and there our people took up their quarters." The military engines and provisions were brought soon afterwards by the fleet, and it was not long before the siege started. The footmen marched against the castle, and a sharp skirmish took place. It lasted about an hour and several were killed or wounded. The men-at-arms hastened to sustain the footmen or infantry in breathless silence, and "then there might be seen such kind of stones thrown, as if they would beat hats and helmets to powder, and break shields and helmets in pieces; for to kill and wound was the game at which they played. Great shouts were among them when they perceived that any mischief had occurred." At this stage of the enterprise several knights distinguished themselves — the "good Bertram de Montbouchier", with him Gerard de Gondronville, an "active and handsome bachelor, who threw up many a stone, and suffered many a heavy blow."

The first body engaged in the assault was formed of Bretons, and the second of soldiers of Lorraine, who rivalled each other in their heroic achievements, and pushed their way to the ditches. At that moment the soldiers of Sir Thomas de Richmont passed close up to the drawbridge, and summoned the garrison to surrender, but the only answer was a discharge of ponderous stones and other missiles. Sir Robert de Willoughby was wounded in the breast by a stone, and the valour of some other knights is specially mentioned. Ralph de Gorges fell "more than once to the ground from stones and the crowd, for he was of so haughty a spirit that he would not deign to retire." Sir John Fitz-Marmaduke was "like a post, but his banner received many stones, and many a rend difficult to mend." Sir Robert Hamsart "bore himself so nobly, that from his shield fragments might often be seen to fly in the air:" and "the good Baron of Wigton (John de Wigton) received such blows that it was the astonishment of all that he was not stunned, and, without excepting any lord present, none shewed a more resolute or unembarrassed countenance."

Stones flew as "thick as rain;" blows were alternately given and received; and there were few that "remained unhurt, or brought back their shields entire."

The whole narrative in reality bears a strong resemblance to the storming of Front-de-Boeuf's castle in "Ivanhoe". The soldiers actively engaged were reinforced by the followers of the King and of the Prince of Wales, who conducted themselves with the greatest gallantry. Sir Alan de la Forde mined the walls with considerable effect, and many a heavy and crushing stone did Sir Richard de Kirkbride receive. Of this knight it was said "so stoutly was the castle assailed by him that never did smith with his hammer strike his iron as he and his did there." The soldiers emulated the gallantry of their leaders, and were indefatigable in their assaults on the massive stronghold.

The bravery and perseverence of the besieged were no less conspicuous. They showered upon their assailants such "huge stones, quarrels, and arrows, and with wounds and bruises they were so hurt and exhausted, that it was with very great difficulty they were able to retire." At this juncture Lord Robert Clifford sent his banner and many of his retinue, with Sir Bartholomew de Badlesmere, and Sir John Cromwell, to fill the places of those who retreated. But the besieged did not permit them to remain long; and when this party also retired, Sir Robert de la Warde and Sir John de Grey renewed the attack, but the garrison was prepared to receive them, and "bent their bows and cross-bows, and kept their espringalls in readiness both to throw and to hurl."

The fierce retainers of the Earl of Brittany restarted the assault, supported by the followers of Lord Hastings, and soon covered the entrance to the castle. The courage of the garrison was not subdued. We are told that as one of them became tired another took his place, and they defended the fortress the whole of one day and night, and until about nine o'clock in the morning of the following day, but the numerous stones thrown from the robinet "without cessation, from the dawn of the preceding day till the evening," depressed their courage. They were further intimidated by the erection of three large battering engines "of great power and very destructive, which cut down and clave whatever they struck;" and every stroke, by "piercing, rending, and overturning the stones, caused the pieces to fall in such a manner that neither an iron hat nor wooden target" could protect them. The erection of these battering engines was the chief cause of their surrender. Finding resistance to be hopeless, and some of their number killed, they requested a cessation of hostilities, and hung out a "white flag", but the soldier who waved it was shot by an arrow. The rest demanded mercy, surrendered the castle, and surrendered to the King of England. The Marshal and Constable of the King of the English forces immediately ordered hostilities to cease, and took possession of the place. Soon after, the banner of Edward, with those of St Edmund, St George, and St Edward, and those of Segrave, Hereford, and Clifford, waved over the towers of Caerlaverock.

The English were amazed to find that the garrison amounted to only sixty men, and if we are to credit our poet's statement, Edward behaved, on this occasion, with great clemency, not only pardoning but rewarding this gallant band. "They were all kept," he says, "and guarded until the King commanded that life and limb should be given to them, and ordered to each of them a new garment." But in the Chronicle of Lanercost the account of their fate is entirely different, and it is affirmed that Edward ordered many of them to be hanged. As soon as the Castle surrendered, Edward proceeded to Galloway, where he stayed for some weeks, visiting Kirkcudbright, Twynham, Fleet, and other places, and making several votive offerings to the altars in churches to the saints, for their fancied assistance after the capitulation of the castle.

He returned to Caerlaverock on the 29th of August, where the Archbishop of Canterbury had come at the express command of the Pope with an epistle in favour of the Scots, recommending peace. This led to a truce, and Edward finally left Caerlaverock for Carlisle on the 3rd of November.

The Castle was entrusted to Lord Clifford who had distinguished himself during the siege. This nobleman served in the third squadron, which was led by the King in person; and the poet who celebrates his valour, says that if he were a young maiden, he would bestow on him his heart and person in consideration of his renown — Clifford was then little more than 25. The fortress of Caerlaverock remained in the possession of the English for several years; and it appears that in 1312, Sir Eustace Maxwell, its then proprietor, joined the English interest, though he soon after distinguished himself in the rescue of Robert Bruce. As a result it was again besieged, and was defended for several weeks before the assailants were forced to withdraw. Fearing that it might again fall into the hands of the English, Sir Eustace Maxwell demolished a part of the fortifications, for which he was rewarded by King Robert Bruce. His son, Sir Herbert Maxwell, in 1347, swore fealty to Edward III. In 1353 the castle was taken from the English by Sir Roger Kirkpatrick, who lived in it till he was barbarously murdered in 1357.

Blood and brandy on the smugglers' trail!

Daylight was appearing over the blue hills of Cumberland as the long boat was hoisted on deck, after landing a cargo of gin and brandy from a smuggling brig, which rode at anchor in a bay of the Solway. 'Diaoul am skyppwch!" sung out old Griffyth Llewyn the boatswain, from the mast head, in a tone somewhat between the opening of a fox hound and the growl of a tan-yard mastiff. "Diaoul am skyppwch! Captain Yakens, there's a lofty sail in the offing, and she stands right in for the mouth of the bay — she's a sloop of war by God, with her sky-scrapers and royal studding sails, flying jib and spritsail — topsail with the Union Jack at her mizzen peak." "Pipe all hands to quarters," cried the captain, "cut away the cable by the hawse — put the helm up, and man the foretopsail halyards — hoist the jib and foretopmast staysail." All hands were instantly at work, and the brig was soon under weigh, while amid the creaking of blocks aloft, the yo ho! of the sailors, the voice of old Yakens was heard at intervals, giving the necessary orders to clear the ship for action. "Cast off breechings and muzzle lashings, overhaul the gun-tackles, prime your guns fore and aft, and get your matches lighted, trice up the boarding nettings and see your pikes and pistols ready — the first man aboard that offers to flinch his quarters, shall have my cutlass in his guts."

Besides a goodly tier of twelve pounders on each side, the brig mounted two long eighteen pounder stern-chasers, which Captain Yakens usually called his long Toms. These he ordered to be double shotted with round and cannister, and beside each, he stuck in the deck a linstock, with a match ready lighted. Being prepared to give the cruiser a warm reception, the brig stood out to the middle of the bay. The wind was light and variable, shifting to almost every point of the compass, as is often the case in places surrounded by steep and lofty hills.

Pathways cut through thick bushes in the narrow glens below were the only passes of communication between the shores of the bay and the inland country. On one side, the entrance of the bay was formed by a pile of huge cliffs, whose grey pinnacles overhung the boiling surge, which groaned and weltered among the chasms worn by the tides in their bases. From the foot of a steep hill, on the opposite shore of the bay, a shell bank stretched obliquely towards these cliffs, terminating in a ledge of rocks, which at flood tide were mostly under water. The outermost two of these were known among seamen by the name of Pellocks, due to their resemblance to the shape of that creature, as they appeared above the water at ebb tide. A strange vessel, making into the bay, was very apt to run foul of these Pellocks, and, if it blew hard, to be beat to pieces. The cruiser seemed to have information on the smuggler, for having taken in her small sails, ready for action, she passed between the Pellocks and the cliff, and steered slowly and majestically up the bay. The smuggler stood across, in hopes of being able to get between her enemy and the narrow sound, but was prevented by the cruiser from making an escape. A constant fire of single guns was promptly answered by Captain Yakens. The report of each gun was echoed several times by the surrounding hills. It seemed as if a whole squadron had been engaged. At length a breeze springing up in a favourable quarter, the smuggler resolved to make a bold run for the sound. "Helm a-weather," cried Yakens, "drop the peak — square the main yard — let go the head bowlines — brace about the head yards." Both made for the entrance, firing their broadsides as they bore down. At a short distance from the sound, the smuggler came close alongside her enemy. Old Yakens plucked from his bald scalp the hat and wig, and tossing them on the cruiser's deck, declared,"Take these, you lubberly dogs, for wadding to your guns." The brig shot ahead like an arrow, and firing her long Toms, double shotted, raked her antagonist from bow to quarter, killing several men, and cutting away so much of her running rigging that the sails became unmanageable. Having gained the offing, she stood merrily to sea, slowly followed, but in no danger of being overtaken by the sloop of war.

Meanwhile a strong party of the country people who were involved in moving contraband, were busily employed in carrying off the goods. These were hidden in the glens, in pits dug out under the ground, and covered over with turf, which they called cellars. Having finished with concealing all but what they intended carrying off at that time, they brought their horses from the thickets where they had been tied. Each man assisted his neighbour to load the horses with two casks each, slung in ropes over the back, and fastened under the belly with girths and leather straps. This done, and seeing the coast was clear, they assembled to take some refreshment from their leather-cased pocket bottles, and to settle the particulars of their march. First, it was necessary to appoint a man well mounted, and who knew the country exactly, to ride in front and act as guide. "I'll tell you what, lads," said big Tam Raffle, "there's no a man amang ye kens the country better than I do, an' there's nane amang ye better mounted. I could engage to ride my mare Black Bess, through foord and through flowe, in ony direction, atween Raeberry and Dalmellington, the mistiest day or the mirkest night in winter; an' I'm thinkan," says Tam, poising in his hand a large whalebone whip handle loaded at the end with about two pounds of lead, "there's few o' the kingsmen, wha ken Tam Raffle, would be willing to plant themselves forenent him. It's no a month sin' I grippet by the collars Andrew Rab an' Rough Roger the hulkmen, at Jamie Guthrie's door-cheek at the Abbey-burn, and held their heads to the wa' till two o' our ain folk laided their naigs wi' *the guids,* an' rade aff afore their vera noses." "Just sae, Tam," said Wat Wylie, taking a draught of right Cogniac from a cased bottle which he called his pocket pistol, "just sae, but that was after I

Plunder is brought ashore

had bribed the twasome wi' half a dozen silk Barcelonas, to stan' still an' mak' nae resistance." "Nane o' your jaw, Wylie," said big Tam, "ye're aye readier to crack your joke, than to clour a crown in time o' need — resistance! they kenn'd they were in the gled's clawts." Sure enough, when about half drunk, with one of his large paws on a man's throat, and the other twisted in the hair of his head, Tam was a formidable antagonist, if no lethal weapons came into play; but in all other circumstances, an arrant coward. However as he knew the country perfectly, and was well mounted, he was selected as front rider. But as they stood a far greater chance of being pursued than of being met by the kingsmen, they required quite a different sort of person to bring up the rear.

There was among their number a daring, resolute fellow, called Ivay Macgill. This man seemed to take delight in nothing so much as breaking the laws of his country. Following no regular employment, he was by turns a smuggler, a poacher, a killer of salmon in the close season, and whenever a vessel was wrecked on the coast, Ivay was sure to be on the lookout for plunder. He was tall and sinewy, bearing the appearance of remarkable agility rather than of extraordinary strength. His compressed lips, and small grey eyes, peeping fiercely from under two bushy eyebrows of a reddish tawny hue, marked him out as a man ready to do any desperate deed. In their drunken carousals, he usually sat apart from his comrades, smoking his pipe in silence like one in deep thought; and when the fumes of the liquor had inspired all the rest with mirth and called forth the broad laugh and the smutty song, Ivay rarely smiled, but would contract his brows and seem to be sunk in deeper gloom. That day he rode a strong chestnut horse, and as it was well known that he did not worry about his own life, nor that of any other man, the party unanimously agreed that he should bring up the rear. They all carried heavy bludgeons, or long loaded whip handles; and, beside these, many of them had under their coats instruments somewhat like the blade of a butcher's knife, about eighteen inches in length, shutting into a wooden handle a little longer, with a joint like a common clasp knife. This weapon Wat Wylie called a jockteleg. Having fixed on their line of march, and agreed in case of attack and dispersion, to meet at night in Johnnie MacWhirter's Pub at Clachangate, each man mounted his horse, and, seated between the two casks, began their march up the narrow way which led through one of the passes of the hills. They reached the open inland country, without any appearance of danger. Tam Raffle rode in front, about a gun-shot before the rest of the party, now and then singing a verse of some song to ease the tediousness of the way, and sometimes calling back to his comrades to mend their pace. As he was jogging on and lilting up merrily:

> Whare'er we see a bonny lass we'll ca' as we gae by,
> Whene'er we meet wi' liquor guid, we'll drink an we be dry;
> There's brandy at the Abbey-burn, an' gin at Hestan bay,
> An' we will go a smuggling before the break of day,
> For we are jolly smugglers — — — —

All on a sudden Tam's song stopped, and some of his companions were alarmed to see him cut the slings of his casks, and ride away as fast as Black Bess would carry him. He whipped her with great vigour, and sometimes looked over his shoulder to see if he was getting fast enough out of the reach of some imminent danger. In a little he disappeared in a hollow, which led into the wood of Auchenwhattle, in the recesses of which a whole troop of dragoons would never be able to find him. Presently after Tam's disappearance, Ned Alishender, the next in advance, saw a party of dragoons at some distance, riding briskly across the smugglers' line of march to intercept them on the open plain. Ned immediately halted, and waving his bludgeon to Ivay Macgill, in the rear of the party, pointed towards the dragoons. Ivay was at no loss to understand the signal, and trotted briskly forward, every man halting as he came up to where Ned Alishender stood. Together they

formed a close body, with their horses' heads towards the dragoons. Astonished at seeing the boldness of the smugglers, the kingsmen commanded them to surrender. Macgill, who acted as captain of the band, answered only by a brandish of his bludgeon; whereupon the sergeant who headed the dragoons, ordered his party to fire their pistols over the heads of the smugglers, hoping to intimidate them into submission.
This was answered by a huzza, and another flourish of Ivay's club. The dragoons seeing this, charged furiously, cutting away at the smugglers, who defended themselves with their bludgeons, and with their joctelegs repaid the soldiers for every cut they received. Being more than two to one, the smugglers kept together in a compact body. From their position they could not be attacked any where but in front. Sergeant Bagshaw the leader of the dragoons, enraged at being kept at bay in this way, made a resolute dash and forcing himself into the midst of the smugglers tried to disperse them and open an entrance for his men. As one of the best swordsmen in his regiment, he wounded several of the smugglers severely, but still he failed to break open a passage for his men. For some time he was opposed by Ned Alishender, a powerful man and, next to Macgill the most courageous of the party; but the sergeant, by his superior skill in the use of his weapon, cut Ned on the right shoulder, and his jocteleg fell from his hand. At this instant Ivay Macgill rushed forward, his grey eyes glaring, with their outer corners turned up obliquely like a tiger cat. Without hesitation he attacked the sergeant most furiously. In spite of all his efforts, the dragoon found his sword crossed in every cut which he made, by the smuggler's bludgeon.

With quick eye and ready hand, Macgill warded off for some time the dragoon's blows, and watching his opportunity, with his jocteleg in his left hand (which he could use as readily as the right) by a back blow, cut the counter of his antagonist's horse. The animal reared on the hind legs, and falling the speed they could. At this house Ivay was always a welcome guest, making frequent presents to the guidwife, of a hare, a salmon for a kipper, or a fringed Barcelona for her neck on Sundays; and, if the opinion of the servant lasses might be credited, receiving in return some "favours secret, sweet and precious," when the guidman was from home. Having reached the farm house, the smugglers threw off their loads against the broken end of a peat stack, and pulling down as much of it as completely covered their goods, hid their horses in an old kiln. Baxter and Rorison sheltered in the barn while Ivay disguised himself as a farmhand. Getting a large truss of straw upon his back, and looking as if he were about to feed some cattle, Ivay was right on cue as the first of the redcoats came within earshot. In a pre-arranged signal the guidwife cried out to him: 'Kenned ye yon three riders, Geordie, wha passed here e'en now, an' took the water aboon the chapman steps?" "Atweel no," quoth Ivay, "but I think they wad hae been better employed handling some honest man's pleugh, than scampering the kintra wi' prohibit guids in defiance o' baith law an' gospel, whilk says 'Thou shalt render unto Caesar his duties on brandy an' tobacco'." And away he trudged with his burden. "Which way did these smugglers go when they passed here just now?" said the officer to the guidwife, as he came up. "An please your honour," said she, "they crossed the water aboon the chapman steps, and took the wood, at the braid side, forenent the Wullcat craigs, makin straught for the hie-road that leads to Craigancleugh Brig; an' gin ye dinna ride the faster, they'll cross't afore ye win up wi' them." Away rode the soldiers in the direction pointed out by the guidwife. "De'il speed the hindmost o' ye," quo she; and turning on her heel, she went into the kitchen to prepare toasted bannocks, and a draught of home brewed, for Ivay and his comrades. When they thought it time to resume their journey, the smugglers brought out their horses, and began to reload their goods; but not before Ivay had taken from his pocket a gimlet and quill, and piercing a cask of right Cogniac, filled the guidwife's gardevine to the neck. They made ready for their journey, mounted, and as it was now dusk, trotted away to the nearest road for Johnnie MacWhirter's. They reached Johnnie's, and found that the rest of the party had arrived safely. Their fellows had already stowed away their goods in safe places, and were assembled round the kitchen fire, with plenty of the best liquor the ports of France and Holland could provide. Macgill and his comrades soon joined them, and on telling the particulars of their escape from their pursuers, the whole company toasted the health of the guidwife. "She's a famous mare, your Black Bess," quoth Wat Wylie to big Tam Raffle, who had arrived long before the others, having lost his load, which was the only prize the kingsmen got that day. "She's a famous mare, your Black Bess, Tam. I think she has been broke to the tod-hunting in her youth, she kens the gate sae weel to the cover;" at the same time giving a sly wink across the fire to Macgill. Tam knew that Wylie alluded to his precipitate flight into Auchenwhattle wood, when the dragoons made their first appearance, and taking high offence, swore he would thraw the neck of the first man who offered to pass a jibe on him. "Hoot no," said Bet MacWhirter, a strong limbed broad shouldered lass, and she grasped the tongs in her hand. 'Ye'll no be sae bauld in my father's house. An' I'll tell you what, Tam, gin ye breed ony o' ye're colley shangies here, I'll mak' ye baith black an' blue, an' ye were as muckle as the kirk steeple." "Haud yer jaw, ye brazen faced limmer," said Tam, "or I'll learn ye better manners than yer mither has done;" and seizing Bet by the neck, he began to lug her towards the door. Ivay Macill directed towards him a most iniquitous scowl, from under his tawny eye-brows, and getting to his feet, drew from his pocket a tin case, in which he carried his tobacco pipe, somewhat in the form of a small pistol, and presenting it at

18th century travels in south-west Scotland

Here we reprint extracts from "A Journey Through Scotland" published in 1723. The author had earlier published a similar tour of England. He wrote ....

In five hours from the Isle of Man I arrived at Kirkcudbright, in the Stewartry of Galloway in Scotland.

Kirkudbright is an ancient town, with the prettiest navigable river I have seen in Britain. It runs as smooth as the Medway at Chatham; and there is depth of water and room enough to hold all the fleet of England, so that the Britannia may throw her anchor into the Churchyard. It is also land-locked from all winds; and there is an island which shuts its mouth with good fresh water springs in it, which, if fortified, would secure the fleet from all the attempts of an enemy; but as this harbour lies open only to England and Ireland, it was never worth a government's while to make use of it. The situation of the town is a perfect amphitheatre, like the town of Trent on the confines of Italy, and like it not surrounded with high mountains but a rocky-stony crust, which in this country they call craigs; for they make a distinction here between mountains, hills and craigs. The mountains are very high, rocky, and covered with heath, or heather: the hills are high, not rocky, and covered with grass, through which the rocks appear like a scab. In the middle of this craggy country lies this little town, which consists of a tolerable street, the houses all built with stone, but not at all after the manner of England; even the manners, dress and countenance of the people, differ very much from the English. The common people wear bonnets instead of hats; and though some of the townsmen have hats, they wear them only on

Sundays, and special occasions. There is nothing of the gaiety of the English, but a sedate gravity in every face, without the stiffness of the Spaniards; and I take this to be owing to their praying and frequent long graces, which gives their looks a religious cast. Taciturnity and dullness gains the character of a discreet man, and a gentleman of wit is called a sharp man. I arrived here on Saturday night, at a good Inn; but the room where I lay, I believe, had not been washed in a hundred years. Next day I expected, as in England, a piece of good beef or a pudding for dinner; but my Landlord told me, that they never dress dinner on a Sunday, so that I must either take up with bread and butter, a fresh egg, or fast till after the evening sermon, when they never fail to provide a hot supper. Certainly no Nation on earth observes the Sabbath with that strictness of devotion and resignation to the will of God: they all pray in their families before they go to church, and between sermons they fast; after sermon everybody retires to his own home, and reads some book of devotion till supper (which is generally very good on Sundays); after which they sing psalms till they go to bed.

This, with the adjacent Shire of Galloway, is reckoned to be one of the coarsest parts of Scotland. People form into tribes here similar to the Highland clan system. The Macdweles, Mackys, Macqhys, Maclurgs, Maclellans and Maxwells, are the common names; but gentlemen are never called by their names but, as in France, by their estate: and indeed where so many gentlemen of the same name and surname live in the same county, it would make confusion in business if they were not distinguished by their designations. As for example: I know six gentlemen each called John Maxwell in this Stewartry: when you ask for any, you never name him, but his lairdship, as they call it. A lairdship is ,a tract of land with a mansion house on it, where a gentleman has his residence, and the name of that house he is distinguished by. If you meet a man on the streets, and ask for Mr Maxwell of Gribton, you ask for the Laird of Gribton; but if it is a knight you mention both name and designation: did you see Sir George Maxwell of Orchardton?

I am the more particular in this; because as this is general through the whole Kingdom, I may not be putting you after to the trouble of explanations. There are lairds here of 500 pounds a year, and of 15 only; a Galloway laird of 20 or 30 pounds a year is a frequent thing.

King Charles I erected this ancient borough into a barony, for Mr Maclellan, a gentleman of his bedchamber by the title of Lord Kirkcudbright; but his estate was so exhausted in the service of his royal master during the civil wars, that at the restoration none of the family would take the title; till this last parliament of King George, in 1722, there was such a struggle for electing the sixteen Peers, that a poor man who kept an alehouse in the neighbourhood, and was lineal heir to the title,

A poor man who kept an alehouse is now Lord Kirkcudbright

was persuaded to put in his claim, and accordingly voted, and is now upon the Parliament rolls as Lord Kirkcudbright. There is in the town a good old castle in tolerable good repair, with large gardens, which belonged to the family, but belongs now to the Maxwells.

There is a monument of freestone, with a statue as big as the life, in the Abbey Church of Dundrennon, near this town.

There is fine salmon-fishing in this river, and no place can be finer situated for fishing on the bank of Solway and the north coast of Ireland; but the inhabitants neglect both, there being never a ship and scarcely any boat belonging to the whole town. But the union having encouraged both English and Scots to improve the fishing on the coasts and in the rivers of Scotland, it is to be hoped that this well situated town for that trade may in time come to flourish.

From Kirkcudbright in 24 miles, on the best road I ever knew, being spacious and hard under foot, through this Stewartry of Galloway I arrived at Dumfries. There is neither hedge nor ditch by the road-side, as in England; but wherever you see a body of trees, there is certainly a Laird's house; most of them old towers of stone, built strong, to prevent surprise attacks, which were frequent between the two nations before the union. And two miles outside Dumfries I saw Terragle, the paternal seat of the unhappy Maxwell Earl of Nithsdale, who was taken prisoner at Preston, and made his escape out of the Tower. It consists of a large oval court, in which are very stately apartments and large gardens, suitable to the grandeur of so noble a family. Also within six miles I visited New-Abbey, founded by the famous Dernagilla for the burying-place of her husband John Baliol king of Scotland, whose heart is entombed here; and she called the monastery Dulce Cor, on which Winton, an old Scots poet, made the following inscription:

When *Baliol*, that was her Lord
Spousit, as you heard Record,
His Saul sent to his Creator,
Or he was laid in Sepulture,
She gart apyne his body tyte,
And gart take his heart out quite;
With Spicery right well Savourand,
And of kind wele Flowerand,
That ilk Heart, as Men said,
She balmyt, and gart be laid
In a Coffore of Ebore,
That she gart be made therefore
Enamylit and perfectly Dight,
Locket and bunden with Silver bright,
She foundit into *Galloway*
Of *Cestertians* Order an Abby;
Dulce Cor she gart thame all,
That is sweet Heart that Abby call,
But now the men of *Galloway*
Call that Steid *New-Abby.*

This Dernagilla was daughter to David Earl of Huntington, brother to king William the Lion, and married to John Baliol of Bernard-Castle in Yorkshire; and by her right her son disputed the crown with Robert Bruce, Earl of Huntington.

I passed the river Nith from Galloway to Dumfries over a fair stone bridge of thirteen large arches, the finest I saw in Britain next to London and Rochester. There is a street that leads from the bridge by an easy ascent to the castle, which is on the east of the town. This castle belonged also to the Earl of Nithsdale; and from it the high street runs by an easy descent to the church at half a mile's distance. This high street is spacious, with good stone buildings on each side; those on the north side having their hanging gardens to the river side.

Stone bridge at Dumfries . . .
Finest next to London or Rochester

The Exchange and the Town-house are about the middle of the street towards the south; and besides this great street Lochmaben-street has very good houses. This is a very thriving town, and has a good trade, yet their shipping does not come up within two miles of the town.

This town has been famous for being firmly zealous to the protestant interest ever since the Reformation. The country round this town is very pleasant, and strewed with gentlemen's seats, all finely planted with trees, the great ornament of seats here. Carlavrock Castle, all of free stone, and a fine piece of architecture, on the banks of Solway in full view of England, and the capital of the Earls of Nithsdale, has been a noble seat by its vestiges, which are not so decayed, but they give a full idea of what it was in its glory.

This family is very ancient, for it stands recorded, that King Robert Bruce, contemporary with the English king Edward the First, gave to Sir Eustace Maxwell of Carlavrock twenty two pounds sterling. This was a reward to Sir Eustace for demolishing his castle of Carlavrock, that it might not be made a garrison by the English, and from which they could have annoyed the country. We find also that a Robert Lord Maxwell was sent to France in King James the Fifth's days, and married by proxy, for the King, Mary of Lorrain, daughter to the Duke of Guise: he was Lord of the Bed-chamber, Colonel of the King's Guards, and Warden of the Marches. It is claimed this Lord Maxwell was the chief person Henry the Eighth depended upon, for bringing Scotland under the subjection of England after James the Fifth's death. It is remarkable that this very Lord Maxwell, to convince King Henry of the power he had in the Kingdom, brought in a bill, and carried it in Parliament, for printing and publishing the Bible in the English tongue, notwithstanding the opposition of the Queen dowager and clergy; and yet the family was then, and have been ever since, Roman Catholics.

In King Charles the First's reign we find Robert Earl of Nithsdale a great negotiator in foreign courts; and the Earl who made his escape from the Tower was allied to all the great families in the two kingdoms.

Dumfries stands in the provence of Nithsdale, or the valley of the river Nith; for it is the custom over all the south of Scotland to call the country of each side of a river *dale;* as that on the Tweed, Tweeddale etc. Annandale is a coarse moorish country, chiefly inhabited by the name of Johnston, of which the Marquis of Annandale is chief: his chief seat in this country is Lochhead, near the famous wells of Moffat, that purge like those of Scarborough, and are much frequented, but here there is no raffling, walking and dancing, as at Bath and Tunbridge: a universal quietness reigns in the place.

After I had made this litle excursion into Annandale, I proceeded up the banks of the Nith, through a most beautiful country of about four miles broad on each side of the river, and in twelve miles riding arrived at the palace of Drumlanrig, the ancient paternal seat of the Dukes of Queensbury.

The palace is a square building of fine freestone, with a spacious court in the middle, and a turret, and great stone stairs in each corner: the gallery and chief apartments are adorned with family pictures, and most richly furnished: the offices below are very noble; and the hanging gardens cut out of the rock down to the river side, with water works and grottos, do every way answer the great genius of William, Duke of Queensbury its first founder. There is a vast plantation of trees round the palace, and the surprise of seeing so fine a building in so coarse a country adds to its beauty.

The first of this noble branch of the Douglasses was William Douglas, son to James, Earl of Douglas, who by a deed, which I have seen, gave to him in portion the barony of Drumlanrig in the shire of Dumfries, about the year 1400. The witnesses to this donation are Archibald Douglas, Lord of

Galloway, James Douglas, Lord of Dalkeith, James Lindsey, Lord Crawford, William Lord Lindsey, Robert Lord Colvil, and William Lord Borthwick, *cum multis alijs.* After this donation he was sent on a mission to England to release King James the First then prisoner in London, from whom he obtained a charter, all written by that King's own hand on vellum, curiously done, confirming the Earl Douglas's donation of the lands of Drumlanrig, Hauyke and Selkirk, signed and sealed at Croyden in Surrey the last day of November, 1412. We find this Sir William a great sharer in all the public transactions during that King's absence. He was killed at tha battle of Agincourt, in France, in 1415. We find this family eminent through the whole race of the Stewarts down to Charles the First, who created the Lord Drumlanrig Earl of Queensbury, and Charles the Second created the grandson first Marquis, and then Duke.

THE HILLS OF GALLOWAY

Farewell, ye Hills of Galloway,
Where I've been wont to stray, —
Farewell, ye Hills of Galloway,
My home of childhood's day.
A distant land now claims me,
But thither though I roam,
My throbbing heart will beat with joy
For thee my hilly home!

Ye heathery Hills of Galloway —
Ye woods of oak and pine —
Ye little foaming cataracts,
Ye all are friends of mine:
The eagle haunts your highest peak —
The swan your lake below;
And herds of stately deer are fed
Where Fleet's dark waters flow!

Ye cloud-clapt Hills of Galloway,
Where wildest breezes blow,
The mists of heaven that rest on you,
A weather-beacon show.
The peasant dwelling in the vale,
Reads in each rock and dell,
Aerial lore — vicissitudes
That coming chenge fortell.

Ye ancient Hills of Galloway,
  How changed your aspect now,
From what it was in former times —
  When round your rugged brow
One universal forest waved —
  The native moose-deer's home,
And where the hardy wild Scot loved
  In liberty to roam!

Ye ancient Hills of Galloway,
  How proudly now ye rise
Above the rude and lonely graves
  Of former enemies!
How proudly now your bosoms swell,
  In freedom's present hour —
Though studded close with remnants still
  Of what *was* Roman power.

Ye sea-girt Hills of Galloway,
  How nobly forth ye stand —
As if defying every foe
  To gain your ancient strand.
There's liberty in every breath
  That stirs your forest tree!
There's liberty in every wave
  That greets you from the sea.

Then farewell! farewell! Galloway,
  My blessing with thee rest —
I go to visit other climes —
  I go to be their *guest.*
For not another spot shall claim
  A dearer name from me,
My only true — my native home,
  Sweet Galloway — is thee.